Tip, Sip, Nap

Written by Fiona Undrill

Illustrated by Estelle Corke

Collins

tip

tap

pat

4

tip

5

nap nap

sip sip

tip it

sip it

nap nap

sip sip

11

nip it

tip it

13

After reading

Letters and Sounds: Phase 2

Word count: 20

Focus phonemes: /s/ /a/ /t/ /p/ /i/ /n/

Curriculum links: Understanding the World

Early learning goals: Reading: use phonic knowledge to decode regular words and read them aloud accurately

Developing fluency

- Your child may enjoy hearing you read the book.
- Take turns to read a page, with you reading each left-hand page and your child reading each right-hand page. Try to use a different tone for each page.

Phonic practice

- Turn to page 4. Ask your child to sound out the letters in the word, then blend. (p/a/t – **pat**) Repeat for page 5. (t/i/p – **tip**) Challenge your child to compare the words and point to the letter sound that is different. (/a/ and /i/)
- Repeat for the following pairs of words, identifying which letter sounds are the same and which are different.

  Pages 6 and 7: nap sip   Pages 8 and 9: tip sip
- Look at the "I spy sounds" pages (14 and 15). Point to the ants, and say "ants", emphasising the /a/ sound. Ask your child to find another thing that starts with the /a/ sound. (e.g. *arrow, apple*) Challenge your child to find more things where the /a/ sound is in the middle of the word. (e.g. *cat, bag, hat, can, magpie*)

Extending vocabulary

- Each choose a character in the book to role-play and describe what you are doing on each page. (e.g. page 2: *I am tipping soil into the pot.* Page 3: *I am tapping the packet to get the seeds out.*)
- Still in role, take turns to mime one of the actions from the book, whilst the other guesses what you are doing.